Winter Fun

By Alex Jordan   Illustrated by David Sheldon

Target Skill Consonant Cc/k/
High-Frequency Words we, my, like

Scott Foresman
is an imprint of

PEARSON

Tap, tap, tap, tap.

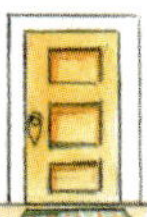

Tam taps at my door.

Tam is cold.

Tam, have my cap.

We pat, pat, pat at snowballs.

We tap, tap, tap at my snowman.

We like the snow.